Goodbye to Angel Island

by Jiang Qingling
illustrated by Dom Lee

HOUGHTON MIFFLIN

BOSTON

Hing Gwong sat up in bed. He had been dreaming of his hometown in China. But as he looked around, the dream faded. Instead of his family's familiar faces, Gwong saw a dormitory room crowded with bunk beds and strangers.

It was very early. Most of the others in the room were still asleep. Rubbing his eyes, Gwong remembered his recent journey across the Pacific Ocean. Just yesterday, after seven weeks of exhausting travel, the boat had docked at a place called Angel Island, close to San Francisco, California.

Although the island's name sounded pleasant, the camp was a frightening place. Armed men in uniforms guided Gwong and other Chinese immigrants off the boat and into a cold, gray building. Inside, everyone was required to register at a booth. Then they were ushered into this crowded dormitory room.

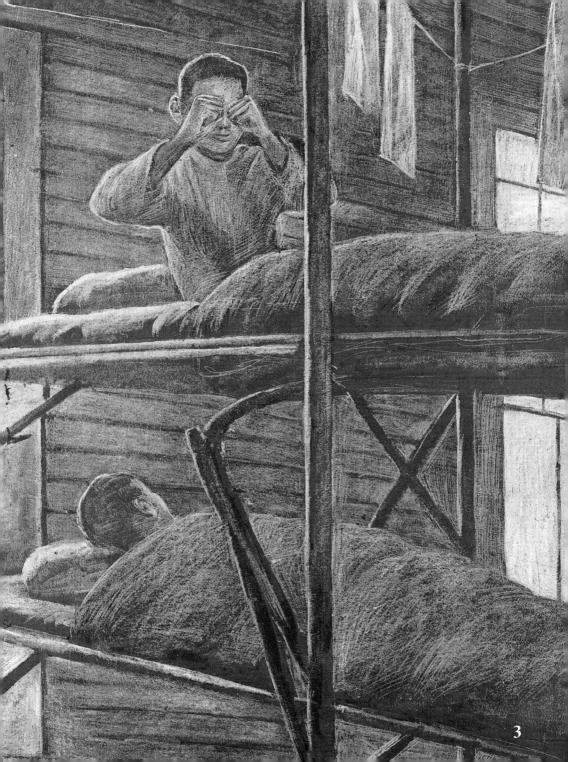

3

From his top bunk, Gwong could see out the window to the beautiful golden hills beyond the bay. To the right of the hills, he could see the city of San Francisco. San Francisco was where Gwong hoped to meet his father.

As he gazed outside, Gwong rubbed a coin in his pocket. Before his father had left for America, he had given the ancient coin to Gwong. His father had traced the coin's history through many generations of their family. He had instructed Gwong to keep the coin with him at all times and said it would bring good luck.

Five years earlier, his father had arrived in San Francisco and found a job at a restaurant. He became a successful chef and gradually saved enough money to send for Hing Gwong, his eldest son.

Gwong felt honored that his father had sent for him. But now he wondered when they would actually meet. His journey across the Pacific Ocean had taken a long time, and now he was stuck in this camp. *How long will I be here?* Gwong worried.

A distant breakfast bell began ringing. Soon, the room was alive with activity. Gwong dressed quickly and followed the other boys and men out the door, down a hall, and into a cafeteria. The aroma of steamed rice filled the large, crowded room.

Gwong joined the long food line, suddenly aware of the growling in his stomach.

"Here," said a boy standing next to him. "You need a rice bowl."

While Gwong mumbled his thanks, the other boy introduced himself. "My name is Lee Pin. What's your name?"

"My name is Hing Gwong."

"How long have you been here?" asked Pin.

"I just came in yesterday. How about you?"

"I arrived last month."

"Last month? You've been here for a month already?" asked Gwong incredulously. The boys moved through the line slowly.

"One month isn't so long," Pin responded. "Some people leave right away, but a lot have to stay for several months—or even longer! I've heard of people who've been here for years!"

Gwong frowned. "I don't understand. Why would people choose to remain here so long? I can't stay—my father is expecting me!"

"People don't *choose* to stay here. Sometimes they're *forced* to stay," Pin replied.

Gwong fell silent at the thought of staying on Angel Island for years. He and Pin quickly sat and ate the watery rice porridge they had at last been served. Then they went outside to the exercise yard.

Gwong blinked in the bright California sunshine. The land was bare, and the buildings were isolated. Barbed wire surrounded the camp. He suddenly felt like a prisoner. *What have I done wrong?* Gwong wondered. He fingered the coin in his pocket.

"How do we get off this island?" Gwong asked Pin.

"You have to wait for the interrogation process," Pin replied.

"What's that?" asked Gwong.

Pin paused before he spoke. "It's a question-and-answer session. If you answer the questions well, you could go immediately. But if your answers aren't satisfactory, you could be stuck here for a long time or even be sent back to China."

"But why do we have to take this test?" Gwong was a little worried.

"A lot of people pretend to have relatives in America," Pin answered. "During a fire in San Francisco in 1906, all immigration records were destroyed. Some people sold false papers to others who wanted to come to America. Now, only relatives of people living in America can legally enter the country."

"Is the test hard?" asked Gwong.

"It depends," replied Pin. "In your case, the right answers are the same ones your father gave. Your father took a similar test when he first arrived. Your answers must match his answers."

Pin continued. "For you, answering questions may be easy. But some people use coaching books to help them prepare for the test."

"A coaching book? What's that?" asked Gwong.

"It lists sample questions that the immigration officers may ask. You can take a look at mine," offered Pin.

Later, back in the dormitory, Gwong looked at the questions in Pin's coaching book. *How many rooms did your house have? Where was the rice bin kept?*

Gwong smiled with relief. These questions didn't seem too difficult.

A few days later, it was time for the boys' interviews. Pin went first. He was in the interview room for more than an hour. As the clock ticked, Gwong grew more nervous. Inside his pocket, he clutched the coin his father had given him. Gwong hoped it would bring him good luck today. Finally Pin came out, smiling confidently. Gwong went in next.

Three stern, uniformed officers sat behind a long wooden table. They took turns barking questions at Gwong. The questions were similar to the ones in the coaching book, and he answered them quickly.

After an hour of answering questions, Gwong began to fidget on his hard wooden seat.

"One last question," said one of the officials, looking sternly across the table at Gwong. Gwong felt his heart begin to race.

"What did your father give you for good luck?" asked the man.

Gwong smiled. "A coin!" he said confidently. "A special coin that belonged to my ancestors."

The next day Gwong and Pin boarded the ferry for San Francisco. As the boat headed toward the city, Gwong looked back. With one hand he clutched the old Chinese coin. With the other he waved goodbye to Angel Island.